NEVER touch A shark!

STICKER ACTIVITY BOOK

Enter a sea-riously cool world
in this activity book!

Search for the hidden sharks,
hunt for treasure and sticker a rock band.

Where there is a missing sticker, you will
see an empty shape. Search the sticker
pages to find the missing sticker.

Don't forget to press out a puzzle
and a pair of shark glasses from the
card pages at the back of the book!

make believe ideas

Volcano view

Search the scene for the things below.
Trace the ticks when you find them.

Count along!

Use colour and stickers to finish the page. Then, count to five!

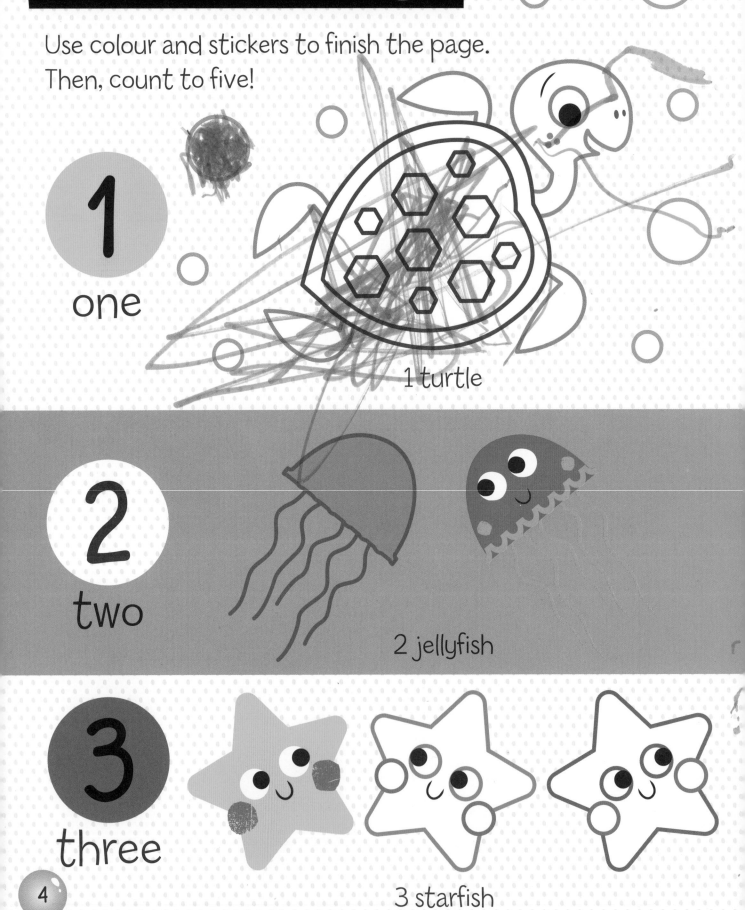

1 one

1 turtle

2 two

2 jellyfish

3 three

3 starfish

4

4 four

4 seahorses

5 five

5 sharks

Sports day!

Use colour and stickers to finish the crowd.

How many yellow flags can you count? Write the answer.

....

6

Follow the lines to see who won the swimming trophy.

Famous fish

Find five differences between the pictures.

Tick the boxes when you find them.

1 | 2 | 3 | 4 | 5

Toy time

Count the toys under each animal.
Write the answers in the circles.

2 ....

....

....

Find me

Find and circle the shark
that looks exactly like this.

Seaweed tangle

Trace the path to guide the shark out of the seaweed.

Start here!

Finish

Shark snacks

Draw a line to match each snack to the correct number.

3

three

2

two

4

four

Treasure hunt

Find the stickers to finish the picture. Then, colour it in.

How many crowns can you count? Write the answer. ....

Shark rock

Use colour and stickers to finish the picture.

Follow the shells

Draw a line to join the shells.

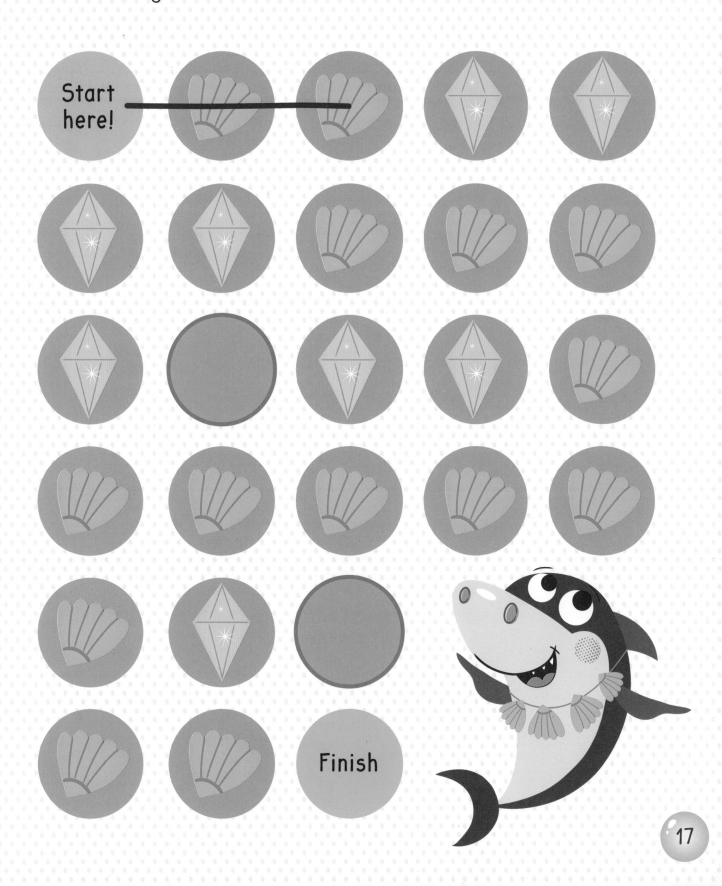

Playful patterns

Find the stickers to complete the patterns.

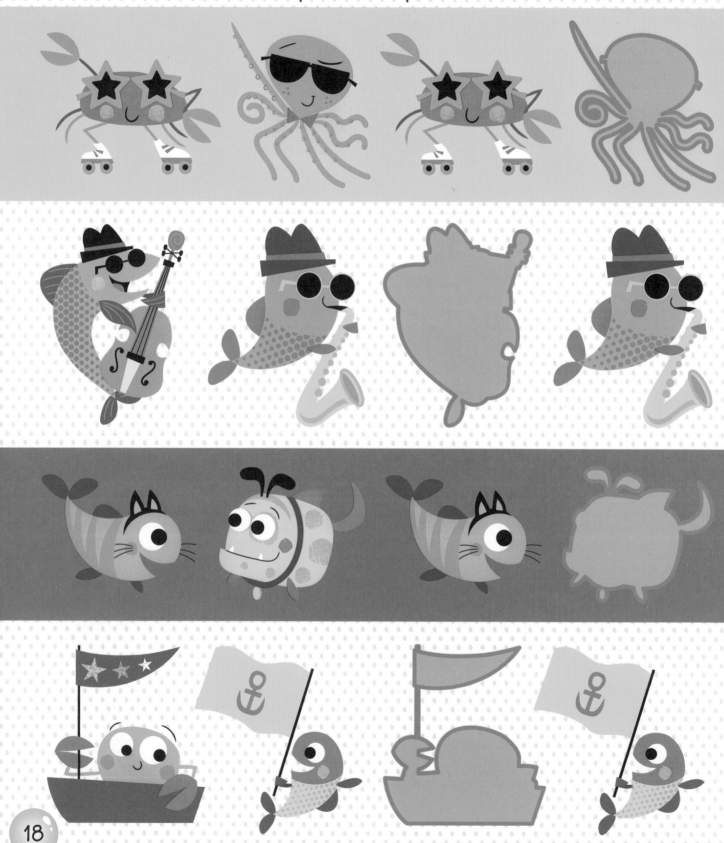

Mini match

Draw lines to match the babies to their parents.

Shark fun

Trace the words to find out what the sharks like to do for fun!

bake

read

race

sing

21

Seahorse sprint

Colour the seahorse. Use the dots to guide you.

Swimming solo

Circle the one that doesn't belong in each row.

Happy homes

Use colour and stickers to finish the page.
Say the colours as you go!

purple

blue

green

orange

Reef party

Search the picture for the creatures below.
Trace the ticks when you find them.

Terrific teeth

Join the dots to finish the shark.
Then, colour the picture.

Sea squad

Press out the puzzle pieces and
mix them up. Then put the pieces
back together to make this picture.

Shark glasses

1. Gently press out the frame, arms, and eye holes.
2. Slot the arms onto the frames.
3. Then put the glasses on!

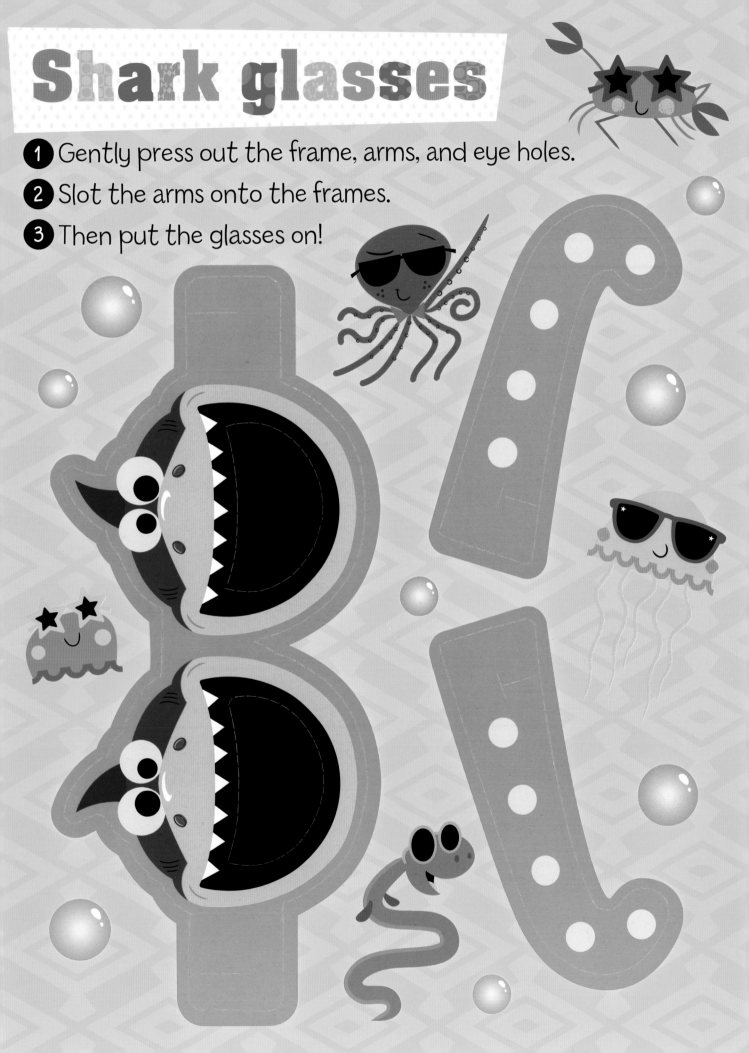

Pages 2-3

Pages 4-5

Pages 6-7

Pages 8-9

Pages 10-11

Pages 12-13

Pages 14-15

Page 16

Page 17

Pages 18-19

Pages 20-21

NEVER touch A dinosaur!

Extra stickers

Page 22

Page 23

Pages 24-25

Pages 26-27

Page 28

Extra stickers